How to use this book

Follow the advice, in italics, given for you on each page.
***Praise** the children at every step!*

Detailed guidance is provided in the Read Write Inc. Phonics Handbook.

7 reading activities

Children:

- ☆ *Practise reading the speed sounds.*
- ☆ *Read the green and red words for the Ditty.*
- ☆ *Listen as you read the introduction.*
- ☆ *Read the Ditty.*
- ☆ *Re-read the Ditty and discuss the 'questions to talk about'.*
- ☆ *Re-read the Ditty with fluency and expression.*
- ☆ *Practise reading the speed words.*

Speed Sounds

Consonants

Say the pure sounds (do not add 'uh').

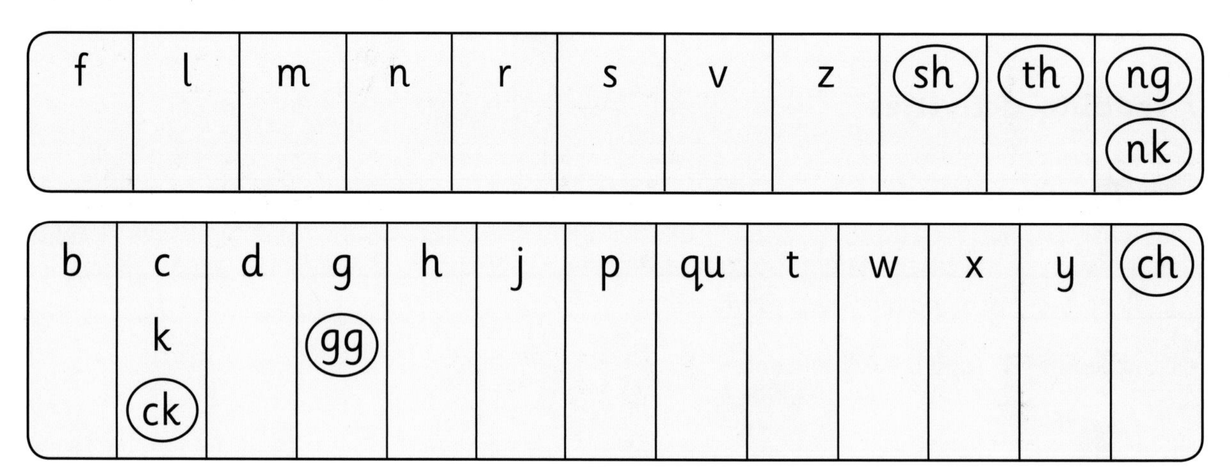

Vowels

Say the sounds in and out of order.

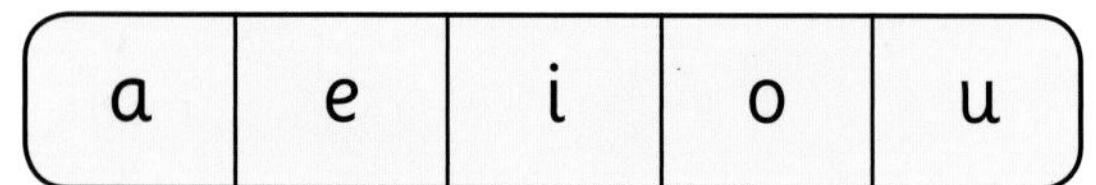

Each box contains only one sound. Focus sounds are circled.

Ditty 1 Cluck

Green words

Read in Fred Talk (pure sounds).

hen pot cluck got hand

hot egg black fresh has

Read in syllables.

egg`cup → eggcup

Red words

my the

Ditty 1 Cluck

Introduction

This is a story about a girl whose hen has laid an egg.

my black hen has got an egg

cluck

in my hand ...

in the pot ...

in my eggcup

fresh and hot

Ditty 2 Munch munch munch

Green words

Read in Fred Talk (pure sounds).

net run big jump plum

lunch crab crunch fresh

fish munch red

Red words

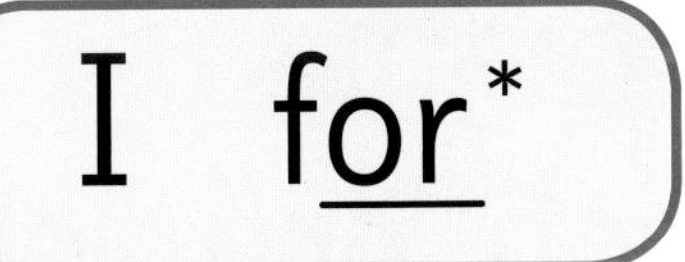

* red for this book only

Ditty 2

Munch munch munch

Introduction

What kinds of thing do you like doing at the beach? In this story a girl goes to the seaside.

I run and I jump

crunch crunch crunch

a crab in a net...

fresh fish for lunch

and a big red plum

munch munch munch

Ditty 3 Splash

Green words

Read in Fred Talk (pure sounds).

can thump stamp drink

swing long trunk splash

Red words

I my

Ditty 3 Splash

Introduction

Have you ever been to a zoo or a wildlife park? In this story we meet an elephant who doesn't like being looked at!

I can stamp

thump thump

I can drink

I can swing my long trunk ...

splash

Questions to talk about

Ditty 1

What colour is the girl's hen?

How does the egg taste?

What is your favourite way to eat an egg?

Ditty 2

What does the girl do first?

What does the girl eat for lunch?

What is your favourite food?

Ditty 3

What does the elephant do at the start of the story to show he is cross?

What does the elephant do at the end of the story?

Tell me what the elephant looks like.

Children practise reading the words across the rows, down the columns and in and out of order clearly and quickly.

Speed words for Ditty 1

hen	got	hand	pot	egg
and	black	my	hot	an

Speed words for Ditty 2

net	run	jump	plum	red
lunch	crab	crunch	fish	munch

Speed words for Ditty 3

can	trunk	splash	stamp
drink	swing	long	thump